Shropshire Meres and Mosses

Nigel Jones

Shropshire Books

Front cover: Berrington Pool, near Shrewsbury (photograph by Bob Kemp)
Back cover: Whixall Moss (photograph by Bob Kemp)

© Nigel Jones 1993
ISBN: 0-903802-56-2

Cover and Book Design: Daywell Designs
Line Illustrations: Kathryn Green
Editing: Helen Sample
Published by Shropshire Books, the Publishing Division of the Leisure Services
Department of Shropshire County Council
Printed by Precision Colour Printing, Telford

Acknowledgements

I have great pleasure in acknowledging the help of a number of people in researching and compiling the information and illustrations for this book.

I am greatly indebted to Bob Kemp for providing so many of his excellent colour photographs, including those used on the covers. Thanks also to Tom Leach, Peter Boardman, Mike Leach and John Reader for so willingly providing photographs. Tony Carr of Shrewsbury Local Studies Library was extremely helpful in locating historical material. Kathryn Green made a magnificent job of the line illustrations in record time. My editor, Helen Sample displayed great patience with me and honed my draft text into shape. Joy Saunders Jenny Mann and Lorna Robson persevered with typing endless amendments to the text. Thanks to Joan Daniels of English Nature for permission to visit Fenn's, Whixall and Bettisfield Mosses Nature Reserve and for assistance in tracking down historical information. Finally my thanks to Gina to whom "Meres and Mosses" became a constant excuse for avoiding my share of household duties.

Nigel Jones

January 1993

The publishers would like to thank the following for their kind permission to reproduce the photographs in this book: Ministry of Defence p.8 (RAF aerial photograph, Crown Copyright); Rowleys House Museum p.10; Shrewsbury Records and Research pp.14, 44 (top); Bob Kemp front and back cover, pp.19 (bottom), 21 White Water Lily, Cotton Grass, Branched Bur Reed, Bog Asphodel, Greater Reedmace, Round-Leaved Sundew, 22 all photos; Tom Leach p.20 Canada Goose, Snipe, Mallard, Moorhen, Tufted Duck; Michael Leach p.20 Coot, Grey Heron, Black-Headed Gull, Great-Crested Grebe; John Reader p.21 Yellow Iris, Grass of Parnassus; Peter Boardman p.21 Southern Marsh Orchid; Nigel Jones p.xiv, 2, 42, 43; Sarah Barker p.11, 44 (bottom).

Contents

About the Author

Nigel Jones studied Geography at Dorset Institute of Higher Education and Countryside Management at Manchester Polytechnic. He moved to Shropshire in 1986 to take up the post of Countryside Management Officer with Shropshire County Council's Leisure Services Department. As part of his work he has produced management plans for The Mere, Cole Mere and Brown Moss. He lives in Shrewsbury with his wife, Gina and daughter Lorna.

Nigel has a long standing passion for natural history which stems from many days wandering the Malvern Hills in his youth. He describes himself as a keen entomologist with a particular interest in hoverflies, solitary bees and solitary wasps.

Foreword

The meres and mosses are arguably the most renowned natural features of Shropshire. This series of hollows in the glacial drift of the Shropshire and Cheshire Plain are either filled with water, the meres, or with peat, the mosses. Together they form a wetland complex which scientifically is of national importance.

The hills of the south and west, the river Severn with its tributaries and the market towns and villages may to many be typical Shropshire countryside but this landscape of the north has its own particular interest and character. There are well-known features like the mere at Ellesmere and many obscure ones like the intriguing Oaf's Orchard stuck out in the middle of the vast peatland of Fenn's and Whixall Moss.

There is much to be explored and this book will provide a useful guide with clear information on the evolution of this unusual landscape and on its natural history. It will provide further insight to the resident Salopian and will introduce the visitor to a fascinating countryside of meres and mosses.

Paul Bell

President, Shropshire Wildlife Trust

Meres and Mosses in Shropshire

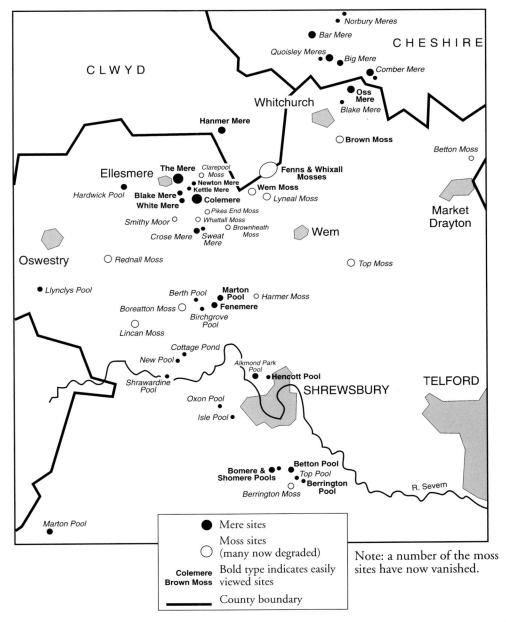

CLWYD

CHESHIRE

Norbury Meres

Bar Mere

Quoisley Meres

Big Mere

Comber Mere

Whitchurch

Oss Mere

Blake Mere

Hanmer Mere

Brown Moss

Betton Moss

Ellesmere

The Mere

Clarepool Moss

Fenns & Whixall Mosses

Newton Mere

Kettle Mere

Wem Moss

Hardwick Pool

Blake Mere

Colemere

Lyneal Moss

White Mere

Pikes End Moss

Smithy Moor

Whattall Moss

Brownheath Moss

Crose Mere

Sweat Mere

Wem

Market Drayton

Oswestry

Rednall Moss

Top Moss

Llynclys Pool

Berth Pool

Marton Pool

Harmer Moss

Boreatton Moss

Fenemere

Birchgrove Pool

Lincan Moss

Cottage Pond

New Pool

Alkmond Park Pool

Shrawardine Pool

Hencott Pool

SHREWSBURY

TELFORD

Oxon Pool

Isle Pool

Betton Pool

Bomere & Shomere Pools

Top Pool

Berrington Pool

Berrington Moss

R. Severn

Marton Pool

● Mere sites

○ Moss sites (many now degraded)

Colemere
Brown Moss Bold type indicates easily viewed sites

County boundary

Note: a number of the moss sites have now vanished.

Introduction

Introduction

Travelling towards Ellesmere from Shrewsbury, just north of
the small village of Cockshutt, you suddenly come upon an area of
small hummocky hills. Here, the landscape changes quite quickly from a fairly flat
plain, dotted with trees, so characteristic of much of north Shropshire, to a gentle,
hilly landscape and then, quite abruptly, you find yourself amongst the small steep-
sided, rounded hills of the Ellesmere area. This is classic meres and mosses country
- a product of the end of the last great ice age.

As you pass through this small but well defined region you will catch glimpses over
hedges and through the trees of numerous quite large lakes. These are the meres. A
glance at the local Ordnance Survey map gives another indication that this is a special
landscape. Names on the map include The Mere, Cole Mere, Pikes End Moss,
Whattal Moss, Sweat Mere, Crose Mere and Clarepool Moss. Nearby is the vast peatland of Fenn's and Whixall Mosses. Casting your eye over a wider area of the map you
will detect a large number of scattered pools as well as several names indicating the
presence of mosses long since gone.

The formation of mosses is a well studied and understood process but many
mysteries to their origins still remain. The formation of the meres, the most visually
striking features of this region, is subject to much conjecture and is not at all well
understood. Much remains to be discovered about these beautiful and fascinating
places. In this short book you will find some simple explanations as to how these
meres and mosses may have formed some ten to twelve thousand years ago. There is
an account of their history gleaned from various sources and a visitor guide to this
relatively little known region, where an inquiring mind can find plenty to sustain it,

Glacial landscape. Typical landscape of the meres with numerous small, hummocky hills, to the north of Ellesmere.

and where those with a discerning eye for the landscape will find much to enjoy on walks around these peaceful meres and through quiet countryside.

Students of the environment are now beginning to take a keen interest in the meres and mosses and in the final part of the book there is an information sources section which I hope will provide a useful starting point for anyone wishing to find out more about north Shropshire's ecological treasures.

The History of the Meres and Mosses

Ice Age Origins

The story of the meres and mosses begins some eighteen thousand years ago, when the last great Ice Age to affect Britain had clothed north Shropshire in an immense sheet of ice which may have been up to one thousand metres thick. Experts do not agree on the exact thickness of the ice sheet but it seems certain that there was a minimum depth of three hundred metres. Even this smaller figure gives a situation where a vast weight of ice bore down on the surface of the land. This gargantuan weight is particularly important in the story of the meres and mosses, for it helped form the landscape which gave rise to the meres and mosses.

It is worth while taking a pause before proceeding with the story to imagine a large slab of concrete say four or five inches thick and about six feet square, being pushed over the ground. The result (apart from a strained back) would be a considerable scraping and loosening of the soil and stones beneath the slab, and a piling up of soil and stones at the front and sides of the slab. Now, just try to imagine the effects on the ground of a huge ice sheet at least three hundred metres thick! To help you, the average tall tree in Shropshire is about twenty to twenty-five metres tall, so think about a sheet of ice towering above you some twelve times the height of your tall tree. If you have ever had to carry a bucket of water any distance you will know how heavy this can be, and ice is frozen water, so as you can now imagine the ice sheet must have pressed down on the land surface with a weight that exceeded hundreds, if not thousands of tons at any one point.

During the Ice Age the ice sheet moved imperceptibly away from its source. In

1

These large erratic boulders, dug up in Oswestry, originated from the Welsh mountains.

north Shropshire there were two sheets moving south and east. The gigantic weight of an ice sheet moving forward would have ground the solid bedrock beneath it to a fine flour like substance. This fine "flour" is known as glacial till. We also use the term to describe the process by which we till the soil to make a fine tilth for growing crops in. Also as the ice sheet moved forward it would have picked up large boulders and rocks, probably snapping off many protruding pieces of rock. These rocks in turn would have been ground along the bottom of the ice sheet, causing further grinding of the bedrock and of the boulders themselves. Today one can find rocks, known as glacial erratics, in Shropshire from as far afield as Scotland and the Lake District - transported here under the great ice sheet.

Caught up in all this turmoil were gravels and sands which often became mixed up with the newly forming tills. All this crushing, grinding and transportation of materials took place over a period of some sixty thousand years. During this time the ice sheet melted at least twice as the climate warmed and cooled again and on such occasions the melt water from the ice washed out and deposited huge amounts of till, sands, gravels and smaller boulders over the land surface. These deposits known by geologists as drift deposits, form an unconsolidated and random mix of material in places. In other places they are of fairly pure sand or sand and gravel mixes. Much of this material would have been washed out at the base of the melting ice sheet, but much was washed out across the top of the ice sheet and some parts of the ice sheet would have been covered in a thick deposit of clay-like tills, sand and gravel (see Figure 1). This factor is important in the second part of the story.

About thirteen thousand years ago Shropshire was experiencing the effects of the end of the last great glaciation of its landscape. The ice melted as the climate steadily warmed. Great melt water streams carried a final load of till, sand and gravel into Shropshire which was laid down over the deposits from earlier warm periods to form a drift deposit, generally of around one hundred metres thickness. This drift deposit is evident as far south as Little Stretton (just south of Church Stretton) and marks the limits of the last great ice sheet.

In places and especially around Ellesmere in north Shropshire there was a local increase in the accumulation of drift deposits of tills, sands and gravels, known as a morainic belt. It is thought that this is connected with a small re-advance of an ice sheet emanating from north Wales. This reached into the area between Ellesmere and Whitchurch. The front of this temporarily advancing ice sheet would have pushed additional deposits forward as well as piling previous deposits up rather like the edge of a bulldozer. These deposits were left behind as the ice sheet finally retreated back towards Wales, leaving a belt of glacial moraine. The result is the ice moulded landscape of hummocks and hollows described in the introduction.

The scene is now set for the next stage in the formation of the meres and mosses. Between thirteen thousand and ten thousand years ago the landscape was overlain by large depths of loosely compacted deposits. Some were very free draining (sands and gravel), some were relatively impervious to water (the clay tills) and in between were mixes of both the sands, gravels and tills giving rise to intermediate conditions. The random and complex arrangements of sands, gravels and tills within these drift deposits gave rise to water tables at varying depths. For example the occurrence of a band of clay impedes free drainage through sands and gravels and causes the water table to remain high in the normally free draining deposits above it. In places the coincidence of a high water table with a depression in the hummocky landscape gave rise to open water in the depression - the beginnings of a mere. Sometimes these hollows would have arisen as a result of the undulating landscape - a natural feature

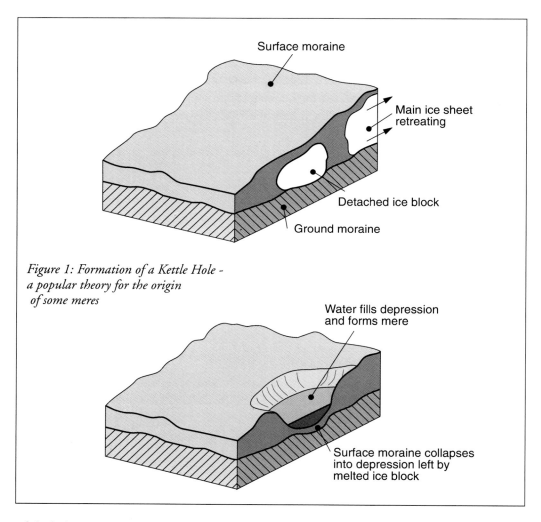

Figure 1: Formation of a Kettle Hole - a popular theory for the origin of some meres

of drift deposits especially of those around Ellesmere.

Elsewhere the ice had a further role to play in producing features known as kettle holes, which are popularly believed to be the origin of many, but not all meres. As the ice retreated large blocks of ice became detached from the main ice sheet. A detached ice block would have been left surrounded by drift deposits underneath and around it, with similar deposits, termed surface moraine, overlying it. The block of ice would eventually melt and leave a hollow into which the overlying deposits collapsed (see Figure 1). This hollow would have been characteristically steep-sided and deep, as some of the Meres are, notably: Bomere Pool near Shrewsbury, Kettle Mere and Blake Mere near Ellesmere. The mere at Ellesmere is in one place over eighteen metres deep but elsewhere is much shallower. This may represent a kettle hole which formed within an existing hollow in the landscape.

These hollows soon filled with water. Initially there would have been plenty about from the outwash from the melting ice sheets and for a time large areas of Shropshire lay under a series of lakes, including a substantial one named Lake Lapworth. At this time the landscape of north Shropshire must have been completely characterised by water and wetlands. As these lakes drained away the underlying landscape was exposed again and many of the hollows would have remained full of water.

After the Ice Age - Meres or Mosses?

How they developed

The meres are not supplied with water from streams and rivers. In the main they are fed by a process known as groundwater percolation. Next time you pass a building site or road works where a ditch or hole has been excavated take a look at the water which invariably accumulates in the bottom of the excavation. The level of water is controlled by the height of the water table in the ground in which the excavation is made. This is exactly the same process which fills the meres.

With the passing of time the hollows developed in two ways. Some into meres characterised by open water (there are around fifty in a region including parts of Cheshire, Staffordshire, Clwyd and Shropshire. The majority of these are in Shropshire - about three dozen) and some into mosses characterised by accumulations of peat.

As soon as the climate warmed up enough to cause the ice sheet to melt, conditions were suitable for plants to grow in and around the meres. At first Shropshire would have been home to tundra vegetation, similar to that found in Siberia and other

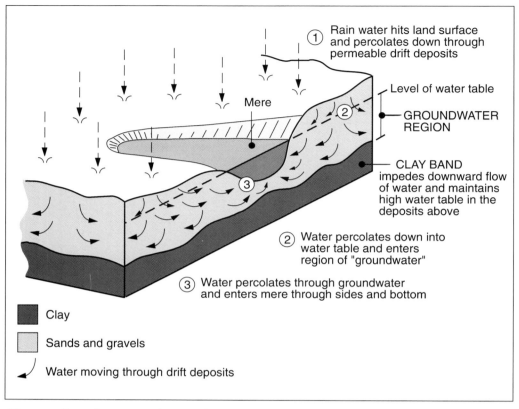

Figure 2: Groundwater percolation - showing how water leaches through the ground into a mere.

northern latitudes today. We know this because pollen, preserved in peat and lake sediments over thousands of years, indicates what was living and growing at a particular time. Scientists are able to date organic matter by a process known as radio-carbon dating. Dating is possible by this method to an accuracy of within a few hundred years.

The most celebrated find of organic deposits in Shropshire was at Condover where the bones of an adult and three juvenile mammoths were found during sand quarrying operations. The mammoths appear to have died in a kettle hole, in which they became stuck about twelve thousand, seven hundred years ago.

The location of the mammoth find illustrates well the processes which take place over thousands of years in a kettle hole. At Condover the remains of the mammoth were overlaid by silts and peat. The silts would have been washed into the hollow from the surrounding landscape. Before the mammoth wandered into the kettle hole it already had an accumulation of clay silts in it. The peat would have accumulated as vegetation grew, died and failed to rot away. Thus each year a new layer of dead vegetation grew and died on top of the last year's. Over thousands of years this amounts to a considerable depth of peat. At Condover two metres of clay and peat lay over the mammoth. This peat incidentally, contained the remains of red deer and a bear.

An artist's impression of the young mammoth trapped in a kettle hole at Condover, about 12,700 years ago.

Vegetation can fill in open water quite rapidly and where this rots down reasonably well a lush fen will develop around the edge of a mere. In a classic case, at Sweat Mere in north Shropshire, the original open water has almost completely vanished, having been progressively invaded by fen. This process would be fairly rapid in shallow basins where plant roots can easily establish in the basin bottom. In steeper sided basins (such as kettle holes) the process is slower, with the far more gradual

Sweat Mere. Photo taken in 1954. The original pool is almost completely overgrown. In the water are Water Lilies, around the edge a floating raft of Greater Reedmace, behind which are stands of Willow and Alder trees.

accumulation of silts causing infilling. Thus many open waters are still apparent as the meres we know today.

The mosses on the other hand have become more or less completely infilled by the remains of vegetation in the form of peat. The vital factor in the formation of peat is a lack of nutrients, giving rise to very poor, acidic, waterlogged soils. Such conditions are termed anaerobic and are characterised by a singular lack of oxygen in the water-logged soil.

To understand in simple terms what may have happened to produce mosses, where instead meres or fens might have developed, it is useful to return to the meres and consider the nature of the water entering these water bodies via the process of groundwater percolation.

As water seeps through the ground it passes over many particles, and organic salts are dissolved into the water. When the water reaches the mere and percolates through the bottom and sides of the mere, it is relatively rich in dissolved organic salts. It is naturally nutrient rich, an unusual feature of any area of open water. The meres are regarded as unique water bodies in Britain, being of Ice Age origin and naturally eutrophic (nutrient rich). Indeed there are few other such freshwater bodies anywhere in the world. Similar lakes only occurring in Poland, Germany and Denmark in Europe, and Minnesota, Wisconsin and Indiana in North America.

So how do nutrient poor, acidic, deoxygenated conditions arise in hollows which normally give rise to almost the opposite? What appears to have happened is that in some shallow basins layers of partly decomposed vegetative material have been laid down and this has acted as an impervious barrier to the nutrient rich groundwater. The groundwater cannot seep through these deposits and deprived of the source of essential nutrients and salts the character of the water changes gradually (or even quite speedily), becoming very acidic. Once this happens the conditions for the development of peat bog are in place. Eventually the layers of peat rise above the surrounding water table, isolating plants even more from the nutrient enriched ground water. In these conditions Sphagnum mosses are the dominant plant growing on the juvenile moss. With the lack of oxygen and very nutrient poor, acidic conditions, the bacteria so vital in the decomposition of organic matter cannot thrive. A well aerated compost heap by absolute contrast is teeming with bacteria. Before one

The "Ellesmere Punt". An ancient dug out canoe found at Whattal Moss, buried and preserved beneath six feet of peat. Now at Shrewsbury Museum.

year's growth of plants has properly decomposed, another year's dies on top of it, further compounding the poor conditions by sealing off the lower layers to oxygen at the surface.

Preservation in the peat is so good that trees, plants, insect bodies, skeletons and pollen are all still recognisable even after many thousands of years, as were the Condover Mammoth skeletons described earlier. Other important finds in the peat have been a series of dug out canoes of ancient but uncertain age found at Whattal Moss, Hordley, Loppington, Knockin and at Marton near Chirbury. The best preserved, the "Ellesmere Punt", was found under six feet of peat.

At Whixall Moss a man's body was found in 1889 at a depth of about five feet, so well preserved that his whiskers and nailed boots were still evident. The body was

Birch invading Whixall Moss. Drainage of the moss for peat extraction has lowered the water table, permitting Birch quickly to colonise the drying moss.

interred in the church yard at Whixall. It is thought that the body may have dated from the Iron Age, although unfortunately due to its hasty burial it will never be possible to confirm this.

In time as the surface of a peat moss rises above that of the surrounding water table, conditions gradually dry out at the surface, eventually permitting birch, gorse, broom and heather to establish. Where the water table is lowered by drainage works as has happened in many instances in the last few centuries, this process is of course brought forward dramatically.

Enter Man

At first the landscape of north Shropshire must have been very inhospitable to man. Large tracts of what were considered wasteland dominated the scene - marshes, heathland and of course meres and mosses. The mosses in particular were far more extensive than they are today. Ordnance Survey maps covering north Shropshire hint at the former extent of mosslands. Where once there were mosses but now little remains except plantation woodland or even agricultural land, names like Whattal Moss, Harmer Moss, Baggy Moor, Tetchill Moor and Top Moss litter the map and hint at the wide distribution of mosses and marshes in former times. A visit to these sites today would reveal little more than relatively sterile pasture or coniferous plantations. Drainage represents a triumph for the agriculturalists. In one area, the Weald Moors (to the north of Telford), a vast moor has been reclaimed, beginning with drainage work in the sixteenth century. Drainage and reclamation of the mosses and moors is however a sad end for these inhospitable wildernesses with their long histories linked right back to the Ice Age.

The meres by comparison have suffered to a far lesser extent than their moss counterparts. The main form of exploitation appears to have been fishing but even so a few meres have been drained and reclaimed for agriculture. Most notable is a reputed pool of two hundred or so acres near Wem (this is about twice the size of the largest of Shropshire's present day meres - the mere at Ellesmere), which was drained and converted to meadow:

> *"The old pool was comprehended under the demesne. It contained about two hundred acres of boggy, or marshy ground, formerly overgrown with withys and ollers, and the greater part of it in all seasons of the year usually overflowed with water, so that it was not passable for men, nor cattle. There the tenants and burgesses of Wem had free common of pasture, it being all waste ground till the first year of Queen Mary 1553, when some parcels of it were inclosed ......"*

Garbett S., (1818) History of Wem and Adjacent Townships

Garbett goes on to describe the successive inclosure and drainage of the pool in five major phases between 1553 and 1619.

Richard Gough's famous work - Memoirs of the Parish of Myddle (written 1700, published 1875), describes the drainage of Harmere between 1607 - 1640:

"And first Haremeare yielded great plenty of silver coulered eels beeside an abundance of other fish .... Haremeare Moss was incompassed round with the water of this meare; howbeit, the neighbours did gett some turves (a reference to the cutting of peat turfs) upon it, which they carried over the water in boats; butt Sir Andrew Corbett caused a large causey (causeway), or bank, to be raised throw the water, so that teames and carts might easily passe from Haremeare Heath to the Mosse, and the turves (which before were had freely) were sold at 8d a yard .... afterward, Sir Andrew Corbett and Mr Kelton caused this Meare to be loosed and made dry, and converted it to meadow and pasture."

In addition a nearby mere, Myddle Pool suffered much the same fate in 1600.

Thankfully the majority of meres have survived to the present day and even though most of the mosses have suffered considerable degradation and in many instances have been more or less completely lost, there are still a few examples left, of which, Fenn's, Whixall and Bettisfield Mosses now form a Nature Reserve, thanks to a long and hard fought campaign by conservationists to save it, when it was threatened by the peat extraction industry.

The peat industry in north Shropshire merits a mention here, for it has been going on for some hundreds of years at Fenns and Whixall Mosses and is an important part of the recent history of the mosses. Piecemeal cutting of peat for fuel and as part of small scale reclamation schemes has probably taken place at Fenn's and Whixall since the eighteenth century. The peat was probably burnt locally by those who cut it and their neighbours. Latterly it has been used widely in the horticultural industry.

In 1823 an award was made to reclaim Fenn's and Whixall Mosses but little effort appears to have been made. Later the Dutch lent a hand. They were experts at land drainage in a country where it was almost a way of life to create polders from low lying waterlogged areas frequently inundated by the sea. The Dutch organised drainage and cutting on a regular and well planned basis, so that by the twentieth century production had soared. At a time when machinery was a rarity they of course employed men to cut peat by hand and extraordinarily the practice of handcutting peat survives until the present day. Elsewhere in Britain large machinery milled peat

Peat cutting at Fenn's, Whixall and Bettisfield Mosses. This photograph, taken in about 1960 shows a peat stack of hand cut turves. The turves would be left out to dry before milling or being used as fuel. Note the flat-bedded barrow specially constructed for this work.

at an alarming rate and it was the introduction of such methods at Fenn's and Whixall in 1989 which alarmed conservationists so much and lead to the campaign to save the site.

Handcutting is now fairly rigidly controlled by English Nature who manage the mosses for nature conservation. It is nonetheless quite gratifying to think that this relatively antiquated practice still takes place and it certainly adds character to the mosses.

The Meres and Mosses Today

The Meres - Fertile Lakes

As water percolates through the ground it passes over and around all the sands, gravels, silts and rocks buried in the glacial drift which contains a tremendous range of minerals such as limestones, dolerites and calcareous sandstones (i.e. alkaline or lime-like in status). The water is enriched by dissolved salts e.g. calcium, bicarbonate, sodium, chloride, which are the most common 'salts' and others such as magnesium, potassium, silicate and phosphate. The whole process can be compared with a coffee percolator, whereby water passing through the ground coffee fines picks up the taste of the coffee. Groundwater passing through the glacial drift picks up the 'taste' of the minerals in the ground.

The result of all this enrichment of the water before it enters a mere is an exceptionally fertile lake. The region experiences fairly low rainfall, and most meres receive very little or no surface water from streams or rivers. The water in the meres therefore remains undiluted, ensuring year round nutrient rich meres. In such conditions the growth of aquatic lifeforms is prolific and there is an incredible abundance of what we shall term, for easy reference, plankton.

The plankton consists of blue green algae, which produce the well known breaking of the meres, of which

Water Mite. These small red invertebrates are predatory, feeding on other small invertebrates such as Water Fleas and Midge Larvae.

15

more later, rotifers (very minute multi cell animals), water fleas which feed on the blue green algae, and red water mites - distant relatives of spiders.

The water fleas (they are not a flea or even insects, but tiny semi-transparent crustaceans), especially species of the genus Daphnia, are particularly abundant. So much so in fact that in one investigation eighteen students from Ellesmere College towed a nylon plankton net with a collecting bottle at one end a hundred yards through the water, to find that their collecting bottle was absolutely jam packed full of Daphnia. The water in the bottle was described as "having the consistency of porridge!"

Water Flea

A larger invertebrate feeding on the water fleas and other very small lifeforms is the midge larva, known as phantom larva. The phantom larvae have the ability to float to the surface or drop to the bottom of a mere and are very common in these waters.

All this mass of food in the form of water fleas, rotifers, midge larvae etc makes for good numbers of larger invertebrates such as water-louse, dragonfly and damselfly larvae, water boatmen and water beetles. Curiously the slightly larger invertebrates are proportionately less common than might be expected from the abundance of food occurring at the bottom of the food chain. It is a feature of the meres that they hold enormous populations of plankton, consisting of relatively few species and large, but by no means vast, populations of larger insects, consisting of even fewer species. Numbers are impressive but variety is not. It is probable that the unusually fertile conditions are not suitable for many species designed for the much less fertile waters normally encountered. However, there is still ample diversity to entertain any student of fresh water biology.

A word here about the breaking of the meres, a famous phenomenon which occurs each summer. As the weather warms, the activity of the blue-green algae increases. In particular the algae rise to the surface in vast numbers so that the whole surface of the mere can appear carpeted in a green scum, especially near the edge where it may pile up. The process can be very rapid occurring in only a few hours. Breaks seem to be associated with calm days when lack of turbulence allows the algae to float to the surface. The term break comes from an analogy with the breaking of yeast in the brewing industry which was formerly well established in Shropshire.

Fish

There is very little written information available on the fish of the meres, but most meres appear to have a similar composition of species.

The most common fish is probably the Roach, feeding on plant material and invertebrates. Perch were formerly more common but the "Perch Disease" of the early 1980's hit Perch populations quite severely and to date they have not made much of a recovery. Perch are partly carnivorous, feeding on smaller fish including their own young.

Perch

The other principal fish of the meres is the Pike, a fearsome predator which is quite capable of taking most fish. In the meres it appears to favour Bream, and even birds such as gulls when they are roosting on the water. Bream feeds on weeds and small invertebrates and is found reasonably frequently. It is a long lived fish often reaching over twenty years of age. In 1977 a survey of fish found that Bream born in 1959 were still a significant proportion of the total population, indicating that good years for young Bream are few and far between. Studies in 1983 showed that Bream bred successfully only in 1959, 1966, 1969 and 1973 in The Mere at Ellesmere. Finally Tench probably occur in most meres. This is a bottom dwelling fish, living in stagnant waters. The female lays a staggering nine hundred thousand eggs in the breeding season between May and July.

Researchers from Manchester Metropolitan University have found that the growth rates of fish in the meres are exceptionally high, reflecting the abundance of invertebrate food present. There are certainly a few very large Pike lurking in some meres. In 1978 a local angler landed a 24lb Pike at Ellesmere. At Cole Mere visitors reported seeing a fully grown Black-Headed Gull being pulled under the water by what could only have been a Pike of considerable proportions!

The fish populations of the meres hold significant scientific and conservation value. The larger meres have probably not had their natural populations altered to any great extent by the practice of stocking from outside sources. This is because it is uneconomic to try to stock such large waters for angling. The larger meres, such as The Mere and Cole Mere, therefore probably hold genetically fit populations of coarse fish, well worth conserving as examples of relatively natural populations of freshwater fish.

What You Can See - *at the Meres*

There is of course a great variety of plants and animals to be found in Shropshire's meres and mosses. Experienced naturalists may be familiar with most of the species, but this section describes for the layman the commonest species which will be readily encountered in the field. Mention is also made of some of the rarities and specialities, for these are often the special points of interest at many sites.

Plants

Charles Sinker in his excellent and detailed introduction to the north Shropshire meres and mosses (North Shropshire Meres & Mosses - a Background for Ecologists) divided the meres into two categories, "unfringed meres", that is those with very little vegetation growing in the water around the edge, and "fringed meres", those with good stands of water plants around their perimeters. Even around unfringed meres there are small stands of the commoner plants growing out of the water and muddy edges.

Chief amongst the taller plants, Greater Reedmace, *Typha latifolia* occurs on most meres. It is readily identified by the rather fat cigar-like flower head at the top of the tall single stem. Reedmace grows with its roots under water, but cannot stand submergence below about two feet.

Hanmer Mere

Whixall Moss

▲ Canada Goose

Mallard ▲

▲ Black-Headed Gull

Moorhen ▲

▲ Tufted Duck

Heron ▲

Great-Crested Grebe ▲

Coot ▼

▼ Snipe

▲ White Water Lily

Southern Marsh Orchid ▲

◀ Yellow Iris

Bog Asphodel ▲

▼ Grass of Parnassus

Greater Reedmace ▲

Branched Bur-Reed ▲

▼ Round-Leaved Sundew

▼ Cotton Grass

Downy Emerald Dragonfly

Large Heath Butterfly

White-Faced
Dragonfly

Great Raft Spider

Bog Bush Cricket

One of the commonest waterside plants is the tall grass, Common Reed, *Phragmites australis*, which can grow up to nine feet, but more normally about five to seven feet high. It flowers late in the year, from late August to October, when its dark feathery flower heads can make an attractive display around mere edges.

Common Reed and Greater Reedmace often form pure and extensive stands either by themselves or intermixed with one another.

One thing the visitor to the meres might notice about the plants along the mere edge is that they grow in fairly well defined zones according to the depth of water. In front of the Reedmace and Common Reed, out in the water up to about four and a half feet depth, you can sometimes see a broad band of Bulrush, *Schoenoplectus lacustris*. People often mistakenly call the Greater Reedmace, Bulrush. Bulrush can grow up to nine feet in height but is often shorter. Traditionally the stems of this plant have been cut and dried for use in making rush mats or for thatching roofs. The pith from the stems has even been used in making paper - a truly versatile plant.

In shallower water, nearer the edge of the mere, you will find a good variety of water plants, including the attractive Branched Bur-Reed, *Sparganium erectum*. The flowers of this plant are grouped together in spherical clusters, arranged along the branching stems of the plant and look most attractive when in flower, sporting bright white to yellow colours.

Greater Reedmace

An easily recognised flower is the Yellow Flag or Yellow Iris, *Iris pseudacorus*, which grows in shallow water and permanently waterlogged soil, never at any distance out into the water. It is common around many meres. Flowering from May to July, it is easy to recognise with its yellow flowers of the typical Iris type.

Out on the water you will see the familiar water lilies. Both Yellow Water Lily, *Nuphar lutea* and White Water Lily, *Nymphaea alba* occur quite commonly on the meres. These two plants are specialists of the deeper water up to five feet depth. They have special spongy tissue known as *aerenchyna* which helps take air down to the

23

lower parts of the plant under water. The large leaves of lilies are a familiar and well known sight.

Specialities of the meres include the Least Water Lily, *Nuphar pumila,* found nowhere else in Britain south of the Scottish border; Marsh Fern, *Thelypteris thelypteroides,* the beautiful Grass of Parnassus, *Parnassia palustris* and Cowbane, *Cicuta virosa* - one of our most poisonous plants. The latter two plants are both rare throughout Britain.

When visiting larger meres it will often be noticed that one shore is very lacking in fringing vegetation. This is caused by the effect of wind fetch across the larger meres. The wind piles up the water into a not insignificant wave which constantly erodes away at the base of any establishing plants, preventing the firm establishment of extensive stands of vegetation on the shore facing the direction of the prevailing wind.

Birds

Collectively the meres of north Shropshire, along with the rest in the north west Midlands, are regarded as very important for wildfowl. Whilst no single Shropshire site holds great numbers of any particular species, there are significant numbers spread across all the meres. For instance, on average 120 Teal, 220 Wigeon and 120 Pochard may be present during the winter on the north Shropshire meres. Mallard are abundant, numbering up to two thousand birds on the group of eight Ellesmere meres alone.

For the novice bird watcher the meres are an excellent place to get to grips with water birds and the colour plates show a selection of the most conspicuous birds to be encountered.

Herons are frequently seen flying in the area on their way between feeding areas and nest sites. Their diet consists mainly of fish with occasional frogs, young water birds, mice and voles. There are thought to be around a hundred and twenty pairs in Shropshire (1992) mainly associated with the meres and river valleys. You can see herons easily in the heronry at Ellesmere.

The most abundant large bird is the Canada Goose which you can often approach very closely, especially at Ellesmere where the birds know no fear of man! This large black, buff and grey bird has increased in numbers dramatically since it was first introduced to Britain in the eighteenth century. It is now a considerable pest in ecological terms, being responsible for wholesale grazing and destruction of waterside plants, especially Bulrush, on some meres.

The Mallard is perhaps our best known duck. The male, with a blue bar on its flank and dark green head, is easy to recognise. Another distinctive and easily recognised species is the Tufted Duck. It is a dark bird with a broad white patch on its flank. The Tufted Duck dives for its food and can sometimes be seen swimming under water in shallower areas, especially at Ellesmere.

The Great Crested Grebe is a distinguished looking bird. With a small crest at the back of its head, it is well worth watching out for and is nearly always present on the larger meres especially Ellesmere, Blake Mere and Cole Mere.

Black medium sized birds abound on some meres. These will be Moorhens or Coots. The Moorhen is very common and readily identified by its red forehead and thin white stripe along its flank. The other bird will be a Coot which is even easier to identify with its white forehead and bill.

Mute Swans will need no introduction and are a common sight. Over fifty may congregate at Ellesmere in late summer.

Finally the Black-Headed Gull is present all year round and makes large roosts on some meres, particularly Ellesmere and Cole Mere. It has been estimated that eighteen thousand birds roost on Ellesmere at peak times during winter.

Great Crested Grebe. In spring the adult sometimes carries its young on its back.

Dragonflies and Damselflies

Insects specialising in open water habitats might be expected to proliferate on the meres and they do. A visit to any mere on a sunny day in summer should provide numbers of bright blue damselflies, usually the Common Blue Damselfly, *Enallagma cyathigerum* or the very similar Azure Damselfly, *Coenagrion puella*. It is not unusual to see large numbers of both species in the rank vegetation close to and around meres.

Of the generally larger dragonflies there is always a chance of seeing a Hawker Dragonfly, most probably the large blue and greeny-yellow coloured Southern Hawker, *Aeshna cyanea* or the equally large Brown Hawker, *A. grandis*, which, as its name suggests, is predominantly brown in colour. Both are spectacular insects. You will see a host of other species on some meres, particularly the smaller meres with plenty of fringing vegetation, which is essential for many dragonflies. The best meres harbour over a dozen species giving them exceptional conservation value for these marvellous insects.

The Mosses - Acidic Wastelands

By absolute contrast to the meres, which are eutrophic, ie. fertile, nutrient rich water bodies, the mosses are oligotrophic, ie. very nutrient poor and acidic. The mosses are not however barren by any means, in fact they are home to a wide range of uniquely adapted plants and animals.

The peat is formed when conditions become waterlogged and acidic. This leads to very poor availability of oxygen in the soil which greatly restricts the activity of bacteria, vital in the breaking down of organic matter, this causes a great lack of nutrients so that most plants cannot withstand the inhospitable conditions in peat bogs.

What You Can See - *at the Mosses*

Plants

Sphagnum mosses are the chief plants of this habitat. The habitat is termed

Sphagnum bog in view of the dominance of these plants, which can survive in very acidic pools. Sphagnum soaks up water like a sponge and can re-wet quite easily if it dries out in hot summers. Many of the associated plants described here grow on a floating mat of Sphagnum.

One of the most interesting plants is the Sundew, which has found a novel way round the lack of nutrients. The leaves are covered in sticky hairs, which trap small insects. The Sundew then digests the unfortunate creatures. There are three species of Sundew in Shropshire: Round Leaved, *Drosera rotundifolia*, Greater, *D. anglica* and Oblong Leaved, *D.intermedia*. Only the Round Leaved is likely to be encountered, the other two are very rare in Shropshire. Another carnivorous plant, confined to Whixall Moss in Shropshire, is the Lesser Bladderwort, *Utricularia minor*. It is an insignificant plant with small yellowy flowers that floats in shallow ditches and pools. It has small bladders on its leaves which open to trap small invertebrates. In autumn the bladders fill with water and the plants sink to the pool bottom.

Lesser Bladderwort - now confined in Shropshire to Whixall Moss.

Three kinds of heather occur on the mosses. The real bog specialist is the Crossed Leaved Heath, *Erica tetralix*, whilst Bell Heather, *E.cinerea* and the Common Heather, *Calluna vulgaris*, confine themselves to the driest parts of the mosses.

A beautiful plant of the bogs is the Bog Asphodel, *Narthecium ossifragum*, with its bright yellow star like flowers. It is a real gem to come across on sphagnum bogs or associated waterlogged grassland.

One of the most characteristic plants of the mosses is the aptly named Cotton Grass, *Eriophorum spp.*. Its long white shaggy seed heads look just like cotton and a large stand of it is quite eyecatching in the sun.

Birds

Snipe and Curlew find the mosses ideal
habitat. The long bills of both birds are
designed for probing in soft ground -
abundant on the mosses. The delightful
bubbling call of the Curlew has a strong
association with these wild landscapes.
Occasionally there are sightings of the
rare Nightjar but unfortunately this bird
has not bred in Shropshire for many years.

Curlew

Invertebrates

The invertebrates of the mosses include some real Shropshire rarities. One of the
finest is the Great Raft Spider, *Dolomedes fimbriatus*. This spectacular spider is the
largest British species and despite its size hunts over
pools which it can walk across with ease.

The White Faced Dragonfly, *Leucorhinnia dubia*
has one of its few English strongholds at Whixall
Moss. This rare dragonfly lives in pools with plenty
of Sphagnum moss amongst which the larvae hunt
for prey.

The Large Heath Butterfly occurs on two of the
Shropshire mosses, its most southerly location in
Britain. The butterflies on Shropshire's mosses are
of a particular southern race, showing brighter and
darker markings than the normal race.

Great Raft Spider

Finally, the Bog Bush Cricket, *Metrioptera brachyptera*, a
handsome cricket with its very long antenna, dark colour
and bright green stripe is another bog specialist. It feeds on other insects which it
generally hunts amongst the Cross Leaved Heather. Like all bog specialists it is an
uncommon insect throughout Britain.

Discovering the Meres and Mosses

Many of the meres and mosses are privately owned but you can see a number from roads and rights of way while a few are fully open to the public. This section describes the best places to visit.

Without doubt the most rewarding visit you can make is to the Meres around Ellesmere. Here there are two large meres freely accessible to all and good views of several others.

The Meres

Ellesmere Mere

This is the largest of Shropshire's meres, at 114 acres. For those wishing to acquaint themselves with the birds of the meres there is no better place to visit. Coot, Moorhen, Mallard, Tufted Duck, Mute Swan, Canada Goose, Great Crested Grebe and Black-Headed Gull all come very close to visitors in a scrum for feeding. Between March and mid-June you can see the heronry clearly on an island. In spring and autumn there is always the possibility of more unusual birds turning up on passage or over-wintering, such as Common, Arctic and Black Terns, Sandpiper, Pintail and Goldeneye. It is possible to walk about halfway around the mere, with excellent views across the water. There is ample parking at Ellesmere and the main car park (Castlefield) is situated in a steep hollow which illustrates the very hummocky nature of the area excellently.

The Mere at Ellesmere

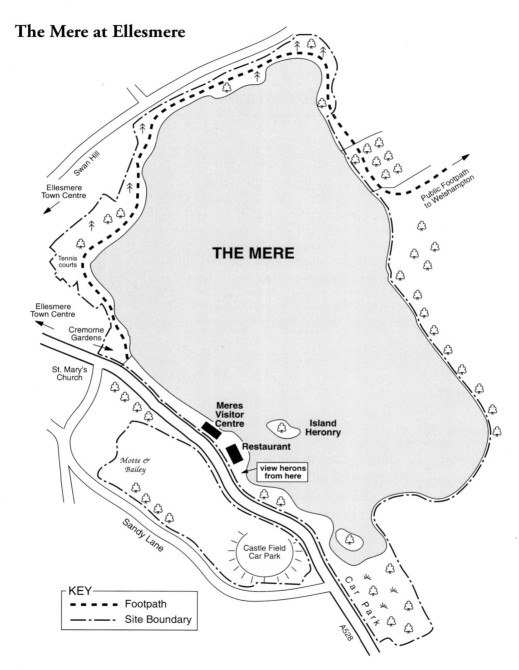

THE MERE

Swan Hill

Ellesmere
Town Centre

Public Footpath
to Welshampton

Tennis
courts

Ellesmere
Town Centre

Cremorne
Gardens

St. Mary's
Church

Meres
Visitor
Centre

Island
Heronry

Restaurant

view herons
from here

*Motte &
Bailey*

Sandy Lane

Castle Field
Car Park

Car Park

A528

KEY
Footpath
Site Boundary

Finding the Mere   This is easy. The mere is alongside the A495 Oswestry to Whitchurch Road immediately east of the town of Ellesmere.

Cole Mere

Cole Mere is a Country Park, open all year round. There is an excellent circuit walk of the mere, through woodlands and meadows.

Plants

The meadows contain a good range of wildflowers. In June/July look out for southern marsh orchid, *Dactylorhiza praetermissa*. This orchid is very locally distributed in Shropshire and is by no means common throughout Britain. This plant is especially important as its world distribution is limited to a small area including Belgium, France and the United Kingdom.

Later in July you may be lucky enough to spot meadow thistle, *Cirsium dissectum*, an attractive, non-spiky thistle. It is another Shropshire rarity and is a speciality of old, poorly drained meadows.

In the mere itself are England's only known colonies of least water lily, *Nuphar pumila*. The best place to view this rarity is from behind a wooden post and rail fence outside the boat compound (see map on page 28).

Birds

Snipe frequently occupy the marshy mere field during the winter. Watch out for their zigzagging flight as they fly off. On the mere itself Great Crested Grebe often congregate in good numbers during winter; as many as twenty-five have been seen at once. All the common species can be seen and, as at Ellesmere, there is always a chance of something special during winter or when birds are on passage in spring and autumn.

Finding Cole Mere   From the A528 Shrewsbury to Ellesmere road, south of Ellesmere, follow road signs to Colemere. From the village follow the brown and white signs to the Country Park.

Towpath walk taking in The Mere, Blake Mere and Cole Mere

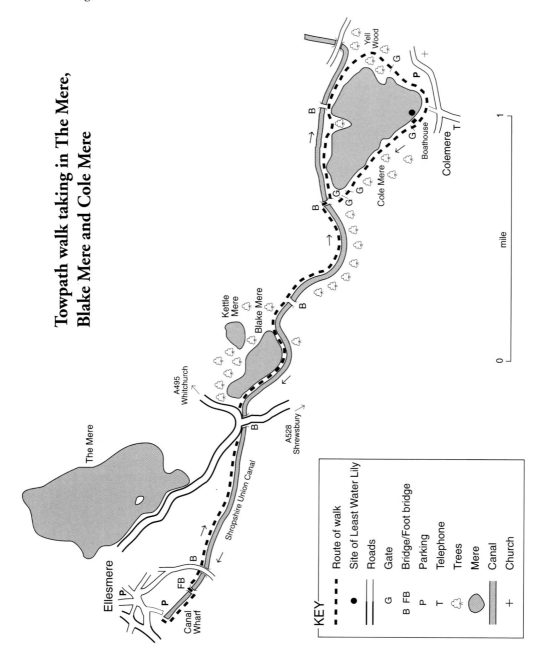

The Mere

Ellesmere

Canal Wharf

Shropshire Union Canal

A495 Whitchurch

A528 Shrewsbury

Kettle Mere

Blake Mere

Yell Wood

Cole Mere

Boathouse

Colemere

KEY

----	Route of walk
●	Site of Least Water Lily
=	Roads
G	Gate
B FB	Bridge/Foot bridge
P	Parking
T	Telephone
🌳	Trees
⬭	Mere
▬	Canal
+	Church

0   mile   1

Day Tours of the Meres

The best way to see more of the meres is by foot or cycle, basing yourself at Ellesmere or Cole Mere.

By Foot

There is an excellent and very easy, level walk between Ellesmere and Colemere along the towpath of the Llangollen canal (see map on left).

This very pleasant walk is quite suitable with a bit of effort for a family with a pushchair. The route takes you around Cole Mere, past Blake Mere, where you should note the steep sided hollow you are walking through - a probable kettle hole - and into Ellesmere town, from where you can walk to the mere quite easily.

Note: Refreshments are usually available in Ellesmere but not at Colemere.

By Cycle

Using Cole Mere or Ellesmere as a base and an Ordnance Survey Landranger map (Sheet 126) it is easy to devise a cycle tour, mainly on quiet minor roads, taking in Cole Mere, White Mere, Ellesmere, Hanmer Mere, Newton Mere, Kettle Mere and Blake Mere.

Your route will take you through attractive, not too hilly countryside and only a couple of short sections are on main roads. Allow for about twenty miles cycling and time to stop and take in the views.

The route   Park at the car park at Cole Mere Country Park. Good views of Cole Mere are available from the car park or you can take a stroll around the mere before you set off on your cycle ride (about 1 hour).

To begin the cycle tour turn right out of the car park and cycle into Colemere village. Bear to the left by Bank House, ignoring the junction on the right. At the next T-junction turn right, signposted Spunhill and Ellesmere. Follow this road for about 1½ miles until you reach a crossroads with the A528.

Just before the crossroads note the extremely hummocky nature of the landscape around you. This is classic mere country. Looking ahead you will eventually catch a glimpse of

White Mere. From this level it is quite obviously set in a hollow in the landscape.

At the crossroads go straight across. (Take great care crossing here. This is a somewhat dangerous junction. Speeding vehicles can be obscured from view by a crest in the road to the left of you.) After crossing the A528 proceed along the road and you will soon pass White Mere on your left. Follow the road to the next T-junction. Turn right, signposted Ellesmere. From here follow the signs to Ellesmere. At the next junction turn right, signposted Ellesmere and over a canal bridge. Follow the road into Ellesmere and turn right into and up St John's Hill, just before a junction in the town. Follow this road along until you reach the A495.

As you ride along this elevated road keep an eye on the landscape to the left of you which again becomes markedly hummocky. In particular you will notice a significant depression which now contains a car park. From here there are good views over the mere at Ellesmere, the largest of Shropshire's meres.

At the junction with the A495 turn left. Follow the main road through the town and turn right into Swan Hill just after a builder's merchants on the left and shortly before a roundabout. This road is followed for about 2½ miles until you reach a junction at Coptiviney. There is a post box on a post here and you should bear right, signposted Breadon Heath and Welshhampton.

Follow the signs to Breadon Heath. At the second junction bear right, signposted Breadon Heath and Welshhampton. Straight over at the next crossroads, signposted Breadon Heath. At the next junction turn left, signposted Hanmer and Penley.

Bear right at the next junction, signposted Hanmer 1¼ miles. On reaching the A539 turn right and then right again into Hanmer Village. You will shortly pass Hanmer Mere on your right. In the village turn right signposted Arowry and Ellesmere.

Shortly after this right junction you will see a public footpath signposted near to a row of bungalows. It is worth while dismounting and following this path for a few hundred yards or so, noting in particular the excellent fringe of vegetation around the edge of one side of this mere. Further on there is also a good example of Alder carr at the mere edge.

Follow the signs for Ellesmere until you reach the A495 where you should turn right, signposted Oswestry and Ellesmere. Take the first left turning off the A495,

Cycle tour of the Ellesmere Meres

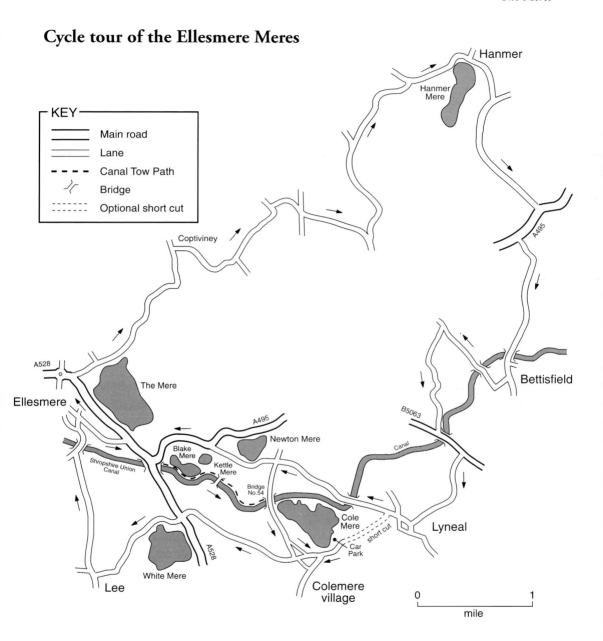

KEY
- ——— Main road
- —— Lane
- - - - Canal Tow Path
-)(Bridge
- ······· Optional short cut

Hanmer

Hanmer Mere

A495

Bettisfield

Coptiviney

B5063

Canal

A528

The Mere

Ellesmere

Newton Mere

A495

Blake Mere

Kettle Mere

Shropshire Union Canal

Bridge No.54

Cole Mere

Lyneal

short cut

Car Park

White Mere

A528

Lee

Colemere village

0   mile   1

signposted Bettisfield and Wem. Proceed into Bettisfield village, and over an old railway bridge then over a canal bridge. Shortly after the canal bridge take the first turning on the right - Knowles Lane. Cross the canal again and at the next T-junction turn left. Cross an old railway bridge and follow the road to its junction with the B5063, signposted Northwood and Wem. Take the next right-hand junction, signposted Lyneal and Colemere.

Cycle into Lyneal and in the village turn right, signposted Colemere and Welshampton. Go straight on, ignoring right-hand junction signposted Welshampton. At the next junction go straight on, signposted Newton and Ellesmere.

Note: If you are feeling tired it is possible to take the left-hand junction here and return quite quickly to Colemere, where you began.

Proceed along the road, crossing the canal and then straight over the next crossroads.

Along this section of road you will pass an area of woodland on your left. Shortly after this, note the area of marsh occupying a hollow in the landscape, also on the left. At one time much of north Shropshire's landscape would probably have been wetlands similar to this, which formed in hollows where the water table was near to the surface.

Proceed along the road and you will eventually pass Newton Mere on your right. Eventually you will come to a junction with the A495.

Dismount at the junction and walk up to the steel barrier on your left. Below you is the aptly named Kettle Mere. Set in a deep hollow it is a classic kettle hole.

Return to your bike and take the left turning from the A495 junction, heading towards Ellesmere.

Take great care along this stretch of road. As you proceed along the A495 look through the trees to your left and you will see Blake Mere below you, also in a substantial hollow.

Just before the junction with the A528 there is a small parking area on your left which you should pull into. Dismount and walk with your cycle down onto the canal towpath below you. On reaching the canal towpath, turn left. Shortly there are very good views of Blake Mere.

From here it is possible to cycle along the towpath back to Colemere. Please note that you should always give way to pedestrians on the tow path and ride with care as the surface can be somewhat rough.

On reaching Bridge No. 54 on the canal, push your cycle up the steep path taking you up onto the bridge to the left of you. Cross the bridge and follow the road, taking the first left-hand junction then the next left and then left again opposite Bank House. From here you return to the car park where you started.

The Mosses

The Mosses are very fragile places and there are very few of them left. Hence access is not available as freely as it is to some meres. Two of the best moss sites are nature reserves and can be visited by permit; Wem Moss and Fenns, Whixall and Bettisfield Mosses.

Wem Moss Nature Reserve

Wem Moss is owned by the Shropshire Wildlife Trust who will issue permits to members and others with a serious interest in visiting the moss. Most notable amongst the many specialities of Wem Moss is the occurrence of all three species of British Sundew.

Details from:
The Head of Conservation, Shropshire Wildlife Trust,
167 Frankwell, Shrewsbury SY3 8LG.

Fenn's, Whixall and Bettisfield Mosses Nature Reserve

Straddling the Shropshire-Clwyd border this enormous moss of over seventeen hundred acres is now managed partly as a Nature Reserve by English Nature, the government organisation responsible for nature conservation in England.

Although the mosses have been extensively dug for peat in the past there are still large areas of exceptional value for wildlife. These mosses form the third largest complex of peat bogs in lowland Britain and as such are of international significance for conservation value.

The sheer expanse of Fenn's and Whixall Mosses alone is impressive, whilst the great variety of bog species is equally impressive. Roundleaved Sundew, *Drosera rotundifolia*, Lesser Bladderwort, *Utricularia minor*, Royal Fern, *Osmunda regalis*, Cotton Grasses, *Eriophorum spp.*, Bog Myrtle, *Myrica gale*, Cross Leaved Heath, *Erica tetralix*, Bog Asphodel, *Narthecium ossifragum*, are amongst the plants to be found. Whilst invertebrates include the Great Raft Spider, *Dolomedes fimbriatus*, White faced dragonfly, *Leuchorhinnia dubia*, Bog Bush Cricket, *Metrioptera brachyptera*, Large Heath Butterfly and a rare caddisfly known only by its scientific name *Hagenella clathrata*.

Visiting Fenn's, Whixall and Bettisfield Mosses   It is possible to view this large moss from a public footpath which runs along the eastern boundary of the site. The site is treacherous in places (Sphagnum bog and very deep ditches can be lethal) and visitors must stay on the right-of-way which can be entered at Ordnance Survey grid reference SJ 504 365, near Moss Cottages.

For those wishing to study the wildlife of the site in more detail apply to English Nature for a permit. Contact: The Site Manager, Fenn's, Whixall and Bettisfield Mosses Nature Reserve, Manor House, Whixall, Shropshire.

Common Cotton Grass. This attractive plant is often one of the first to colonise old peat cuttings.

By far the best way to see these Mosses is by joining the occasional guided tours led by experts who can take you straight to some of the most interesting areas. Another advantage is that there is little danger of getting lost on this vast featureless expanse of wilderness.

Guided walks are usually advertised in programmes of countryside events issued locally, or contact English Nature for details.

Brown Moss Nature Reserve

Brown Moss Nature Reserve is actually a moss with virtually no peat left over its surface. This has been dug off, possibly as early as the sixteenth century, when an award for turbary (peat cutting) was made in 1572. Despite this rather drastic loss of its principal habitat, Brown Moss remains a very important area. The site consists of heathland, woodland and a series of shallow pools which often dry out. The environmental conditions of these pools vary considerably, resulting in a tremendous range of wild plants, including Floating Water Plantain, *Luronium natans*, Least Bur Reed, *Sparganium minimum*, Round Leaved Sundew, *Drosera rotundifolia* and Bog Bean, *Menyanthes trifoliata* all of which are very restricted in their distribution in Shropshire. Floating Water Plantain is threatened throughout the whole of Europe. Least Bur Reed occurs nowhere else in Shropshire and several other plants are uncommon throughout Britain.

Visitors can often see herons feeding on the unfortunate fish trapped in its shallow pools. Amphibians thrive over this predominantly wet site. On one occasion over twelve hundred toads and seventeen hundred frogs were counted on a single day! Amongst the invertebrates are the uncommon Skullcap Leaf-Beetle, *Phyllobrotica 4-maculata* and Red-Eyed Damselfly, *Erythroma najas*.

Access to Brown Moss is easy. The nature reserve is managed by Shropshire County Council and is open at all times. There are two car parks and a nature trail which takes you around the site. Copies of a leaflet on the nature trail are available from Shropshire County Council Leisure Services.

Finding Brown Moss   Take main roads from the south or north of Whitchurch (A49 and A41) and at Prees Heath follow the signs off the dual carriageway for Brown Moss.

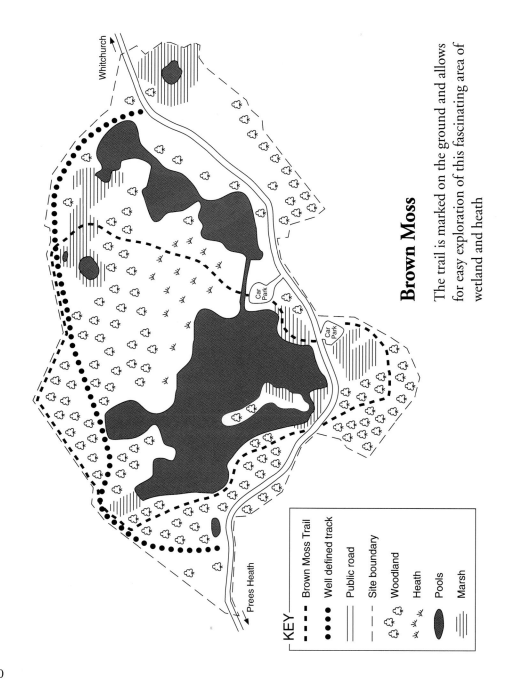

Brown Moss

The trail is marked on the ground and allows for easy exploration of this fascinating area of wetland and heath

KEY

- – – Brown Moss Trail
- ●●● Well defined track
- ‖‖ Public road
- – – Site boundary
- 🌳 Woodland
- 🌿 Heath
- ⬤ Pools
- ‖‖ Marsh

Whitchurch

Car Park

Car Park

Prees Heath

Visiting Other Sites

Several other meres can be reached on the public rights-of-way network. The best ones to visit using Rights-of-Way are:

Site	Ordnance Survey Grid Square	Nearest Town or Village	Comments
Bomere Pool	4908	Bayston Hill	Kettle Hole
Fenemere	4422	Myddle	Partly fringed mere
Betton Pool	5107	Cross Houses	
Berrington Pool	5207	Cross Houses	Fringed mere
Hencott Pool	4915	Shrewsbury	Overgrown mere
Weeping Cross Mere	5110	Shrewsbury	Overgrown mere
Oss Mere	5643	Whitchurch	Partly fringed, fen and carr

Bomere and Betton Pools are a few miles south of Shrewsbury and can be visited on public footpaths. Bomere is an excellent example of a steep sided kettle hole. A footpath leads along the top at one side and gives a good impression of the depth of the hollow the pool lies in. By contrast Betton Pool is situated in a fairly gentle undulation. Both Pools can be reached on a network of footpaths which is best joined at the Burgs, just east of Bayston Hill. A word of warning here, Bomere Pool is home to a large number of voracious mosquitoes and those who suffer badly from bites are advised to visit during the cooler seasons, when mosquitoes are absent.

Berrington Pool is a very attractive site which sits in a classic kettle hole type hollow. The pool is so well ensconced in its hollow that it is only visible from very close range. Berrington Pool is one of Shropshire's very best dragonfly and damselfly localities, sporting rarities such as the Ruddy Sympetrum, *Sympetrum sanguineum* and the Downy Emerald, *Cordulia aena*. There are over a dozen different species at Berrington. The pool also exhibits an excellent fringe of aquatic vegetation which virtually encircles the entire pool edge. Berrington Pool can be reached on a public footpath south of Berrington Hall, just west of Cross Houses. The roadside verge is wide enough to park on, making it an easy pool to reach.

Fenemere, photographed in winter 1992. Note the extensive fringe of reeds growing out of shallow water, behind which is a fringe of Alder and Willow trees on firmer ground.

Hencott Pool is a completely overgrown pool to the east of the A528 Shrewsbury to Whitchurch road. All that can be seen now is Alder and Willow Trees, as the open water has long since disappeared. None the less the site harbours some valuable plant communities, quite different from those found on the open water sites. The site can be reached on a public footpath but there is little to see apart from trees from this footpath. You should not leave the footpath without permission from the landowner.

Fenemere is a good example of a partly fringed mere with good stands of vegetation around its edges. Fenemere can be reached on a public footpath from Myddlewood near Myddle. Nearby Birchgrove Pool is very close to the B4797 road between Baschurch and Marton from where it is easily viewed.

Another pool you can see easily from the main road is Weeping Cross Mere south of Shrewsbury. Although this mere still holds water, trees, mainly Alder, have grown out across it. The pool is very close to the junction of the A458 and the old A5 south of Shrewsbury.

Finally Oss Mere is an excellent medium sized mere to visit. It is set in classic moraine country of small hummocky hills. You can reach it from a public footpath off a minor road out of Whitchurch. As you cross the stile from the road, there is an excellent view of the mere below in a depression in the landscape. Around two thirds of Oss Mere is fringed by open fen with Alder carr behind it, an excellent example of vegetative succession at the mere edge.

Weeping Cross Mere. Trees have now grown across the entire surface of this shallow mere.

Brown Moss. Two views from the same position. The photo above dates from about 1900, the photo below from 1993. There are extensive changes from open water to marsh which has been colonised by Greater Reedmace and rushes, with plenty of succession by Birch trees.

Conservation

Conservation

Wetlands are one of the Britain's most threatened habitats.

Drainage and pollution have taken a terrible toll of our wetlands and we are very fortunate to have such a large number left in Shropshire. However, Shropshire's wetlands have by no means escaped the twin evils of drainage and pollution. The mosses in particular have been drained and reclaimed for agriculture to a very large extent and in recent years the peat extraction industry looked set virtually to finish off the Shropshire mosses. Fortunately the best remaining mosses in the county, Wem and Whixall, are now Nature Reserves.

Drainage of land surrounding mosses does of course continue and at Wem Moss this important Nature Reserve has shown a worrying trend towards drying out. This seems to be linked to local drainage schemes.

There are also problems of drying out at Brown Moss which is not really a moss any more but is none the less a wetland of quite exceptional importance. A large pool here has not held significant amounts of water for a couple of years, and during 1992 remained almost completely dry throughout the year. The cause of the problems at Brown Moss is not clearly established but is very probably linked to the now wide spread practice of water abstraction from bore holes and water courses. In recent years this has been one of the most pressing of conservation issues, with wetlands and rivers drying out all over the country. The result of increased abstraction rates.

The meres, on the whole, have faired better than the mosses, but abstraction and drainage do seem to have affected some meres, most notably Crose Mere, Marton and Bomere Pools which have all suffered a lowering of water levels in recent times.

The most significant problem facing the meres is eutrophication (the enrichment of water bodies with nutrients). Initially the dumping of human and other waste into watercourses started this process, but this has been greatly accelerated in post war years by the widespread use of artificial fertilisers on agricultural land. The fertilisers leach through the water table and into the meres. As the meres are fed almost exclusively by groundwater percolation this can be a serious cause of pollution.

Eutrophication shows itself in an increased number of algal blooms which are often more intense than seems to have been the case in the past. The whole process of eutrophication is insidious and it is difficult to prove the links conclusively between the modern agricultural use of fertilisers and the modern decline in ecological value of meres.

However the changing botanical composition of plant communities in the meres undoubtedly points to a real decline in ecological value in post war decades. In recent times a number of meres have been surveyed at regular intervals (since 1979) by an expert team of botanists and a worrying trend of decline has definitely been established.

Plants which depend on nutrient poor conditions (i.e. oligotrophic conditions) have declined in numbers, some disappearing altogether from some sites. Most notable in this category is the Water Lobelia, *Lobelia dortmanna*, no longer found on any of Shropshire's meres.

Water Lobelia

By contrast plants which do best in nutrient rich conditions (ie eutrophic) have expanded their range on the meres. In some cases they may even be the dominant plants in and around a mere. Examples are Horned pondweed, *Zannichellia palustris* and Greater Reedmace, *Typha latifolia*.

Another threat which grows by the year is the now widespread Canada Goose. This bird does tremendous damage to stands of Bulrush, *Schoenoplectus lacustris*, by grazing the plant to the point of destruction. Any mere which receives the popular attentions of this introduced bird soon shows signs of its collective voracious appetite. Closely cropped grassland around the shore, overhanging trees stripped of leaves to about three feet height, badly trampled and overgrazed marginal vegetation are typical symptoms of Canada Geese in residence. The shores of the mere at Ellesmere and Cole Mere both provide examples of this worrying kind of destruction. Unfortunately it has proved almost impossible for the authorities to take action to stem the growth in the population of Canada Geese. It remains to be seen just how damaging the bird may be in the long term.

There are other pressures on the meres, including use for watersport, particularly waterskiing, and of course there is always the question of increasing visitor numbers to some of the more popular sites. On the whole these problems are small and can be easily controlled. At Cole Mere which receives many thousands of visitors annually it has proved quite possible to manage the site in a way which still permits wildlife to thrive. Even at Ellesmere, which is almost the Blackpool of north Shropshire, there is still considerable wildlife interest, not least a thriving colony of herons in full view of the masses of visitors who walk along the frontage to the mere. The problems of eutrophication and lowering of water table levels are far more serious and will prove far more difficult to control unless there are radical changes in the way our country-side as a whole is managed.

Finding Out More

Finding Out More

The meres and mosses are indeed an ecological and landscape jewel in Shropshire's crown, yet very few people actually recognise this. However, there has been a good deal of research into the meres and mosses over the years and this book has only skimmed the surface of a vast and sometimes complex subject. For students looking for a profitable avenue of study there are many, many opportunities to undertake original research. For someone like myself there is always the fascination of just finding out more about something close to home which is just too interesting to ignore.

Anyone from GCSE to PhD student should be able to make a study of the meres or mosses. Following is a catalogue of sources of information which can get you started on a more detailed exploration of these wonderful places.

Geology and Soils

Toghill P., (1990), *Geology in Shropshire*, Swan Hill Press

Chapter 2 of this book contains a very useful summary of the Ice Age in Shropshire.

Burnham C.P. & Mackney D., (1964), *Soils of Shropshire*, Field Studies Council

This is a reprint from the journal Field Studies (Vol 2, No 1). It contains a useful colour map of soils which shows well the distribution of sand/gravel, boulder clay and peat based soils in the county.

Ecology

Sinker C.A., (1962), *The North Shropshire Meres And Mosses, a Background For Ecologists*, Field Studies Council.

This is another reprint from Field Studies (Vol 1, No 4) and is an excellent introduction to the subject. Despite being some thirty years old, most of the work is still relevant today. This publication does assume a basic level of knowledge of ecology and those without a good understanding of scientific names of plants may find it a bit of a struggle to read. However it is well worth persevering by cross-referencing to a standard wild flower index, which should enable you to pick up the English names for plants mentioned in the text. You really cannot afford to miss reading this if you are seriously interested in the meres and mosses.

Sinker C.A., Packham J.R., Trueman I.C., Oswald P.H., Perring F.H., & Prestwood W.V., (1985), *Ecological Flora of the Shropshire Region*, Shropshire Wildlife Trust.

Apart from being one of the best local floras ever published this book is a must for anyone wishing to know more about wetland plants in Shropshire. Chapter 5 contains a detailed guide to the botany of meres and mosses. There are also distribution maps for many plants showing clearly how heavily many species rely on meres and mosses for their survival.

Reynolds C.R., (1979), *The Limnology of the Eutrophic Meres of the Shropshire-Cheshire Plain*, Field Studies Council.

Another reprint from the journal Field Studies. This is a very detailed and rather technical publication which provides an essential background for anyone researching the water quality of the meres, particularly their chemical composition.

Gabb R., & Kitching D., (1992), *The Dragonflies and Damselflies of Cheshire, National Museums and Galleries on Merseyside*.

Although this book concentrates on Cheshire there are some extremely useful accounts of the dragonfly and damselfly populations of the meres and mosses of Cheshire in Chapter 5. They are very comparable to similar situations found in Shropshire.

Conservation

Shropshire Naturalist Vol 1, No 1, (Spring 1992)

The first edition of this new journal explored Shropshire's wetlands and of course the meres and mosses figured heavily. There are three articles of particular interest - *The Conservation of the Shropshire Meres* by **C. Walker**; *Ponds and Pools of Shrewsbury* by **N. Anderson**; *Fenns, Whixall and Bettisfield Mosses National Nature Reserve* by **A. Hearle**. Copies of this back issue are available from Scenesetters, Bircher Cottage, Little Stretton, Church Stretton, SY6 6RE (Cost about £3.)

Furmage S., (1992) *The Ecology and Conservation of the North Shropshire Meres.* (Unpublished study).

This study is available for reference at the Local Studies section in Shrewsbury Library. The author carried out a comprehensive survey of previous investigations and studies into the meres of north Shropshire. The study is extremely useful as a summary of a whole mass of research and includes a very useful and extensive bibliography. For any students contemplating an investigation of north Shropshire's meres this is an extremely valuable resource.

The County Council holds a master copy of this document and will sell photocopies to interested students. Applications to the Leisure Services Department, Winston Churchill Building, Radbrook Centre, Radbrook Road, Shrewsbury SY3 9BJ.

Other Resources

Site Management Plans

The Local Studies Library at Shrewsbury holds copies of management plans for the following sites:

1. Colemere Country Park - Full Management Plan

2. Ellesmere - Ecological Plan

3. Brown Moss Nature Reserve - Full Management Plan

These management plans are very detailed, particularly those for Colemere and Brown Moss and provide a useful insight into the process of managing these important sites.

Copies of the plans are also available for consultation at some branch libraries in north Shropshire.

Meres and Mosses Study Pack

Finally, the Local Studies Library at Shrewsbury has developed a study pack containing a number of papers from a variety of scientific journals. These are held with the management plans mentioned above.

More Books on Shropshire's Countryside published by Shropshire Books

In the Exploring Shropshire series:
UNDISCOVERED SHROPSHIRE: 14 Walks in North Shropshire,
Eve Powell, paperback £3.50

WALKS WITH WRITERS, Gordon Dickins, paperback £3.50
GREEN WALKS FROM OSWESTRY, Mary Hignett, paperback £2.95

SHROPSHIRE COUNTY GUIDE, paperback £3.50

SOME SHROPSHIRE GARDENS, Barbara Palmer £3.99

CANALS OF SHROPSHIRE, Richard Morriss £4.99

FARMER FEEDS US ALL, Paul Stamper £4.95

For a complete list of Shropshire Books titles please write to:
Shropshire Books, Winston Churchill Building,
Radbrook Centre, Radbrook Road,
SHREWSBURY SY3 9BJ